ViSUaL Literacy

Book 2

Jo Browning Wroe
and David Lambert

Permission to photocopy

The rights of Jo Browning Wroe and David Lambert to be identified as the authors of this work have been asserted by them in accordance with sections 77 and 78 of the Copyright, Designs and Patents Act 1988.

'Someone came knocking' by Walter de la Mare is taken from *The Complete Poems of Walter de la Mare* and reproduced by kind permission of the literacy trustees of Walter de la Mare and the Society of Authors as their representatives.

'What has happened to Lulu?' by Charles Causley is taken from *Collected Poems for Children* and reproduced by kind permission of Macmillan.

Visual Literacy Book 2
MT10784
ISBN-13: 978 1 85503 443 3

© Jo Browning Wroe and David Lambert
Illustrations © Mike Lacey and Matt Ward
All rights reserved
First published 2008

Printed in the UK for LDA

Abbeygate House, East Road, Cambridge, CB1 1DB, UK

Contents

Teacher's notes

This book provides stimulating photocopiable exercises on visual literacy for children from 8 years and up.

What is visual literacy?

You teach your pupils to read so they can interpret written texts and improve their verbal literacy. Pupils are increasingly surrounded, however, by texts of a visual nature. Visual texts use symbols and images to communicate their meaning. Your pupils need to be visually literate to be able to interpret the icons on a computer screen, read a graph, find their way using a map, collect and access data from a chart, or simply cross a busy road safely.

Visual literacy is the ability to interpret a wide range of visual or word texts. The activities in this book ask pupils to take the information they have gained from a visual or word text and respond to it by reformulating it in another mode. To do this, they must engage fully with the content of the text, ensuring comprehension. Better understanding leads naturally to greater text retention. Specific activities in this book are designed to hone the reader's critical thinking skills. The broad range of visual literacy activities presented here in a wide variety of text types (graphs, charts, poems, tables, picture stories, cutaway diagrams, a brochure, maps, timelines) have direct application and relevance right across the curriculum.

The book exposes pupils to three discrete types of text and asks them to reformulate them in one of three different modes:

- ✷ Text to Visual
- ✷ Visual to Text
- ✷ Visual to Visual

Text to Visual

Pupils read a word text and respond to it in the visual mode. For example, grouping the facilities of two holiday camps as a Venn diagram allows them to 'see' similarities and differences that may be less obvious on simply reading about them. Likewise, representing the events of someone's life visually as a timeline requires the pupils to 'see' and graphically 'show' discrete chronological sequences.

Visual to Text

Pupils look at a wide range of diagrams, charts or drawings and respond to them in writing. For example, pupils are given a family tree diagram and asked to interpret the formal relations between the family members as written answers to questions.

Visual to Visual

Pupils are presented with maps, tables, charts and diagrams, and respond in the visual mode. This may involve continuing a picture story, showing a 3D diagram of a building as a 2D plan, or drawing the opposite of an abstract concept.

Follow-up and extension activities

Each of the worksheets has a follow-up activity that requires pupils to answer easily assessable questions on the text (true or false, fill in the blanks, labelling, etc.). Each worksheet also has an extension activity designed to encourage creativity in pupils.

Venn diagrams

Holiday brochures

1 Read the brochures for two holiday resorts, then make a list
of all the fun things you can do in each club.

Pleasure World

Hi, kids!
Welcome to Pleasure World Kids' Club. We've got
a lot of things to entertain you while Mum and Dad do
boring grown-up stuff! Learn to swim every afternoon in
our outdoor pool! If you are 6 or over, you can have a ride
on Daisy the pony! (Don't worry, she's very tame.)

If you've still got any energy after all that, why not come
on a hike to the top of Castle Hill? You can see the whole of
Pleasure World from up there. Can you spot your mum and dad on the beach?

You'll have oodles of fun in the art group, making things with bits and pieces
we picked up on our hike. There's also a treasure hunt and an archery class,
and a game of rounders is always great fun!

Can you sing, dance or tell jokes? Win a prize in our star talent contest!
Well, what are you waiting for? Sign up for Kids' Club NOW!

Sunny Hills

HELLO THERE, BOYS AND GIRLS!
Welcome to Sunny Hills Children's
Club! If you want fun and adventure
on your holiday, sign up for a great
time! Our friendly helpers
Jason and Kelly will take
you on a supervised walk
up Ferndale Hill. You get a
great view from up there!
We have swimming lessons
in the hotel pool with Kelly,
and diving lessons with Jason.

Is go-kart racing more your thing?
We have our own safe mini-track
where you can have a great time.
If that hasn't worn you out, try
trampolining – or why not join in
a game of rounders? With a
treasure hunt and an art
competition, there's
never a dull moment
at Sunny Hills
Children's Club.
Come along
and make your
holiday great!

Pleasure World activities

Pony rides

Sunny Hills activities

2 Write the activities in your lists in the correct circle on this Venn diagram (this makes it much easier to compare the two resorts).

Pleasure World   **Sunny Hills**

3 Now look at your completed Venn diagram and answer these questions.

a) What activities can you find in both holiday clubs? _____

b) Which holiday resort has a talent contest? _____

c) In which resort can you learn to shoot arrows? _____

d) If you liked go-kart racing, which resort would you prefer? _____

e) Which resort has trampolining? _____

f) Which resort has more activities? _____

EXTENSION

Which holiday resort would you prefer to go to? Why?

Chart and mind map

Australian wildlife

1 Read the information about two Australian animals and then fill in the chart.

The Duck-billed Platypus

The duck-billed platypus is found in eastern Australia and on the island of Tasmania. Its habitat is streams and rivers. It is a very odd-looking animal: it is covered in brown fur and it has webbed feet and a beak like a duck. This animal is very odd in another way. Instead of giving birth to live babies like other mammals, it lays eggs. Like other mammals, the mother platypus feeds her babies milk for three or four months, until they are old enough to feed themselves.

The platypus is a carnivore, living on worms, freshwater shrimps and insect larvae.

The male platypus has poisonous spurs on his hind legs to defend himself against predators – which include eagles, owls, snakes and crocodiles.

The Kangaroo

The kangaroo may be found all over the continent of Australia. It lives in grasslands, deserts and forested areas. Early explorers who saw the first kangaroos thought they had two heads because female kangaroos hop around carrying their young in a pouch. The tiny baby kangaroo, called a joey, shelters in the pouch and is very helpless. It feeds on its mother's milk in the pouch until it is 18 months old.

The kangaroo is a herbivore and feeds on grasses and roots. Its predators are dingos, snakes and foxes, as well as humans. Kangaroos can box to defend themselves, but their real danger lies in their kick. One blow from the sharp toenail on a kangaroo's hind leg can kill an enemy.

	Duck-billed platypus	Kangaroo
a) In what part of the world do you find it?		
b) What is its habitat?		
c) What does it look like?		
d) What does it eat?		
e) What are its predators?		
f) How does it defend itself?		

2 Make a mind map.

From what you have learned, make a mind map for the duck-billed platypus.
Write each word in the correct place on your mind map.

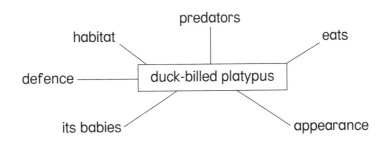

Use these words to get you started

streams and rivers
Tasmania   beak like duck
poisonous spurs
freshwater shrimps
Eastern Australia   snakes
crocodiles   lays eggs
drinks mother's milk
webbed feet   worms
brown fur   insect larvae

EXTENSION
Make a mind map for an imaginary animal.
Give your animal a name and draw it
at the centre of your mind map.

Interpreting a map

A buried treasure map

1 Before he died, the pirate One-Eyed Jack buried his treasure somewhere on St David's Island. Read his instructions to find the treasure and draw your route on the map. Mark the spot with an X.

If you want to find my treasure, follow my instructions carefully! Sail to the west end of the island where the water is deep. Take a route through the very dangerous rocks, called the Seven Sisters. If you make it to the other side, you'll reach Deadman's Bay. Don't steer the ship onto the rocks or you'll be dead men too!

Drop the ship's anchor and swim ashore. In front of you to the east is thick rainforest. Walk through the rainforest and up the tall mountain, Mount King George. At the top you'll find a little stream. Cross the stream and follow it down the southern side of Mount King George. The stream will grow into a big river. Follow it as it turns north.

When you see an old plantation house on the other side, swim across the river. Walk past the southern end of the plantation house or you'll get caught in the man traps for runaway slaves! Walk east, then go through the gateway of the old sugar mill. Go to the east of the swamp ahead, it's full of crocodiles!

When you have made it past the swamp, turn north to the island's northern coast. You will pass a sugar-mill wheel. Out at sea, you'll see a rock called Bird Rock. The treasure is buried on the beach opposite this rock. Start digging! It's all yours!

One-Eyed Jack

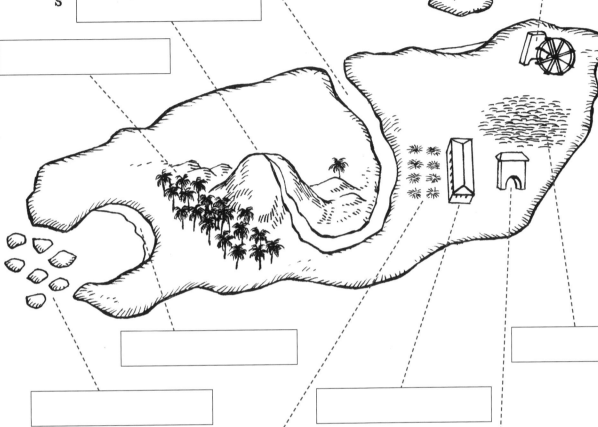

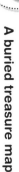

2 Label these places on St David's Island.

The Seven Sisters	the old plantation house	Deadman's Bay
the mill wheel	the rainforest	the gateway to the sugar mill
Mount King George	crocodile swamp	the river
Bird Rock	the man traps	

EXTENSION

Imagine you are a pirate. Choose another place on the island to bury your treasure. Write instructions like these so your friends can find it: start at, head north, continue east, in front of you is, follow, when you see.

Labelling a diagram

Castles

1   Look at this drawing of a medieval castle. What parts can you name?
Read the text and then label the parts.

A castle is designed for defence. Hundreds of years ago, they were built on hills so the soldiers could see enemies coming. The strongest castles had thick walls made of stone. There was often only one main entrance to a castle. A deep moat filled with water usually surrounded it. The moat was crossed by a massive drawbridge that could be pulled up if enemies were in sight. If enemies were swimming across the moat they could not shoot arrows at the same time.

Castles had look-out towers. Often these stuck out. They gave the archers a clear view of their enemies below. Archers could hide, then come out and shoot their arrows from behind battlements at the top of the castle walls. They could also shoot safely from inside the castle through narrow windows called loopholes.

If enemies were captured, they were kept underground in the castle dungeons, from which it was hard to escape.

2 Now write a sentence for each part of the castle you labelled.
Say why the castle had this feature.

Castles had thick walls to keep enemies out.

EXTENSION

Draw the place where you live and label the parts. Under your drawing write a paragraph explaining what each part is for. (Does it have a TV aerial, a garage, a chimney, a garden gate, a lift to reach it, a catflap?)

Matching image and text

Bicycles

1 Look at these bikes. Do you know the names of any of them?

The Tandem *E*_____   The Chopper _____   The Folding Bike _____

The Recumbent _____   The Racer _____   The Dandy Horse _____

The Penny-Farthing _____   The Mountain Bike _____

2 Read the descriptions and write the correct letter beside each bike's name and picture.

Ⓐ Lightweight. The Racer's tyres and wheels are very thin. Drop handle-bars position the rider over the pedals so they can push down hard. Not very robust.

Ⓑ The Chopper has a long front end on small wheels, high handle-bars and a long, curved saddle. Built for style and a smooth ride. The position of the gear lever may cause injury. Popular in the 1970s.

Ⓒ The folding bike is very lightweight. The frame folds up when it's not in use, so the bike can be carried on to public transport. Small wheels mean a rough ride. Not fast.

Ⓓ Heavy steel frame, wooden wheels and steel tyres. Large front wheel and tiny rear wheel mean falls are dangerous. Small straight handle-bars. Known as the Penny-Farthing, but nicknamed the 'bone shaker'. Faster than walking.

Ⓔ Built for one front and one rear rider in tandem. Requires good balance between riders. A tandem is energy efficient. Rear rider has poor visibility.

Ⓕ A recumbent has smaller wheels than a standard bike. Energy efficient. Fast. The lying or recumbent position is relaxing but puts the rider on the level of exhaust fumes. Not always visible in traffic.

Ⓖ Strong thick frame, front and rear suspension for rough or mountainous terrain. Straight handle-bars. A mountain bike has thick knobbly tyres and often has no mudguards.

Ⓗ No pedals. Rider pushes against the ground with their feet. No brakes. Very uncomfortable wooden frame. Faster than walking. Popular in the early nineteenth century. Known as the Dandy Horse.

3 Fill in the chart with the advantages (+) and disadvantages (−) of each bike.

	+	−
Racer	Thin tyres for quick changes.	
Chopper		
Folding		
Penny-Farthing		
Tandem		
Recumbent		
Mountain Bike		
Dandy Horse		

My dream bike design

EXTENSION
In this space draw your dream bike and give it a name. Label the advantages of your bike design. What about the disadvantages?

Bar charts and block graphs

What's your favourite?

The children in Fairville School have collected information on the most popular books in their school library.

1 Read the report they wrote, and show the information as a block graph.

Report on favourite library books

25 children said they liked books about magic

18 children said they liked animal stories most

15 liked books about discovering new parts of the world and space

13 children loved to be scared by spooky stories

6 loved comics because they were funny and easy to read

4 enjoyed reading about the Romans, the Greeks and things from the past

19 could not decide

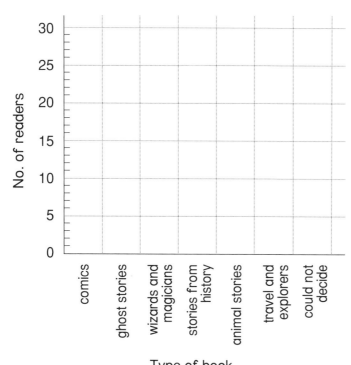

2 A hundred people were asked to name their favourite food. Read the report and show the information as a sideways bar chart.

Report on favourite foods

A quarter of the people said their favourite food was curry.

Ten people said they liked bangers and mash best.

For fifteen people, the most delicious food was fish and chips.

Another ten said they loved spaghetti bolognese most.

Fifteen people said their favourite was roast chicken.

Twenty-five people could not decide.

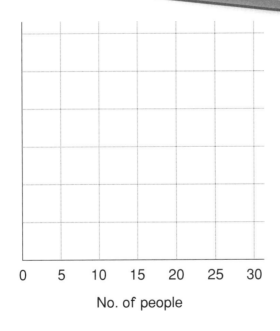

Type of food

0   5   10   15   20   25   30

No. of people

EXTENSION Collect information about favourite foods in your class. Choose a method to display your findings. Write a report based on what you have learned.

Labelling a diagram

Life on an oil rig

1 Look at this drawing of an oil rig. What things can you name?
Read the text and then label them.

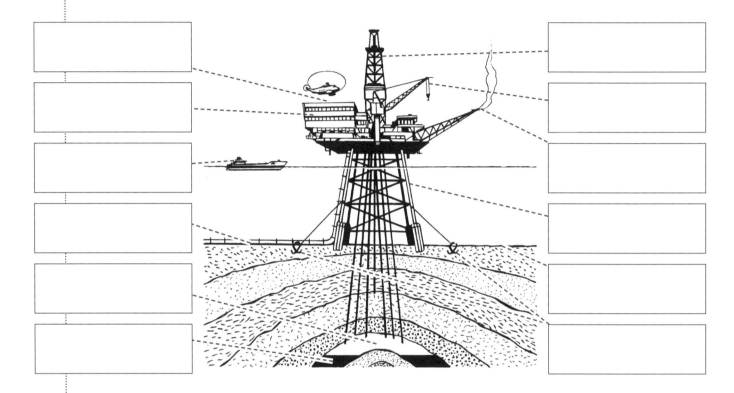

Oil rigs are massive structures which stand on great **steel legs** on the **sea bed**. We have built them there to extract oil and gas from deep below the sea bed. At the centre of an oil rig is the **drilling derrick**. It drills deep through thick layers of rock. **Natural gas** is found at the first level under the rock, and deeper down the drill reaches **oil**. Large **pipelines** take the oil and the natural gas from the oil rig to the shore and to the refinery. Once these fuels are refined, they can be used for cooking, heating our homes and running our vehicles.

Workers on a rig spend months working at sea, with only short breaks at home with their families. The men must be brought to and from the rig by a helicopter which lands and takes off from a **helipad** on top of their **living quarters**. Food and other supplies are brought to the rig by **supply boat** and winched onto the rig by a **crane**.

Out at sea, you can spot an oil rig a long way off by its huge orange flame. If the rig's enormous **burn-off chimney** didn't get rid of this extra fuel, the rig would blow up.

The sea can get rough so, just like a ship, the rig is attached to the sea bed by massive **anchors**. In an emergency, for instance if fire breaks out, the workers must evacuate the rig very fast, so the rig has lifeboats that can be lowered into the water quickly.

2 Now write a sentence for each part of the oil rig.
Say why the oil rig has this feature.

steel legs
drilling derrick
helipad
crane
living quarters
anchors
burn-off chimney
pipeline

a) *The steel legs are what the oil rig stands on.*

b) _____

c) _____

d) _____

e) _____

f) _____

g) _____

h) _____

EXTENSION

Draw an invention that makes our lives easier.
Label the parts. Under your drawing write a
paragraph explaining what each part is for.

Interpreting a map

The slave trade

This map shows the main places where the slave trade took place.

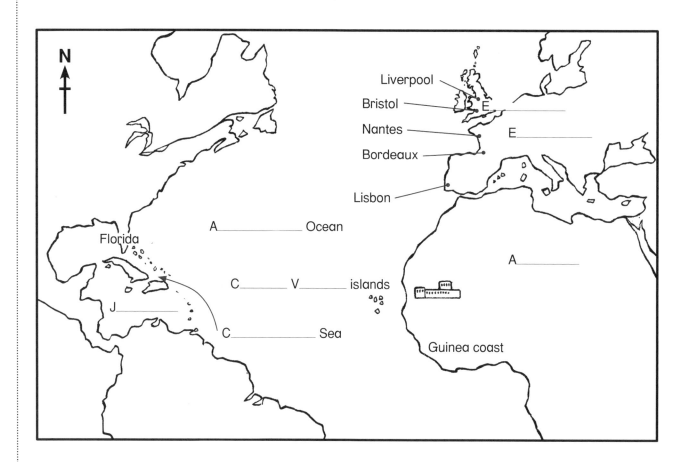

Key to map

The *Ariel's* route

    Stage 1:

    Stage 2:

    Stage 3:

The *Ariel's* goods

    beads:

    guns and gunpowder:

    slaves:

    sugar:

    coffee:

    tobacco:

1 Read the text and complete the map of the slave trade.
Fill in the names of the places on the map.

The transatlantic slave trade was a terrible trade in human beings. Men, women and children were captured and taken from their homes in Africa. They were shipped to the other side of the Atlantic Ocean, where they worked with no pay for the rest of their lives.

A slave ship's route had three main stages. That's why it was sometimes called the triangular trade. For example, in 1750 the *Ariel* left Liverpool in England laden with cheap glass beads, guns and gunpowder. It landed a few weeks later on the Guinea coast of Africa. Here hundreds of Africans who had been rounded up were held in Elmina Fortress. The captain of the *Ariel* traded his guns and glass beads for these human beings as if they were objects.

Then, laden with its human cargo, the *Ariel* set off on the second stage of its journey. This was a long and dangerous voyage across the Atlantic Ocean. The ship stopped only once, at the Cape Verde islands, to take on fresh water. Weeks later the slave ship landed in Jamaica, an island in the Caribbean Sea. The captain of the *Ariel* sold the slaves in markets. The *Ariel* was loaded up with sugar, coffee and tobacco he bought with what he was paid.

On the final stage of its journey, the fully laden *Ariel* left the Caribbean and returned to its home port of Liverpool.

2 Show the three stages of the *Ariel's* route,
both on the map and in the key below it.

EXTENSION Complete the key to the map with your own symbols.
Use colours and drawings to show the features.

Draw your symbols clearly on the map.

Timeline

The history of flight

1 Read the text below.

People have always wanted to fly. When cavemen saw birds flying through the air, they probably tried to copy them by making themselves wings and jumping from cliff tops.

In the fifteenth century, the famous Italian scientist Leonardo da Vinci made a wooden flying machine, but it did not get off the ground. Three centuries later people finally took to the skies, in giant hot-air balloons. The first manned flight of a balloon was on 21 November 1783, when the Montgolfier brothers made the first passenger flight, in France.

But hot-air balloons were slow and difficult to control. In 1903 another pair of brothers, the Wrights, made the first controlled flight in a flying machine. It lifted off the ground in Kitty Hawk, USA, and flew for an amazing 260 metres.

Since the Wright brothers' first aeroplane, flight has developed very fast. On 20–21 May 1927 Charles Lindbergh, an American pilot, made the first solo flight from New York across the Atlantic Ocean to Paris. After the Second World War the new jet engines used in fighter planes were used to fly passenger aircraft. The jets could fly people further and faster. In 1970 the world's largest plane was the Jumbo Jet. It took to the air with a record 524 passengers. A few years later, on 21 January 1976, a plane called Concorde became the first supersonic jet. It could fly passengers between London and New York faster than the speed of sound!

Humans have come a long way from their first attempts to imitate the birds. Who knows what the future holds for flight?

2 Complete the timeline with what happened on these important dates
in the history of flight.

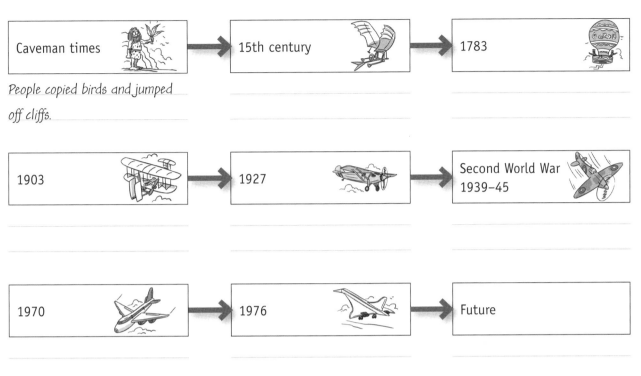

Caveman times | 15th century | 1783

People copied birds and jumped
off cliffs.

1903 | 1927 | Second World War 1939–45

1970 | 1976 | Future

3 On the map draw:

a) the route of the first
solo Atlantic flight

b) the route of Concorde,
mentioned in the passage

c) the route of a flight you
have taken or would like
to take.

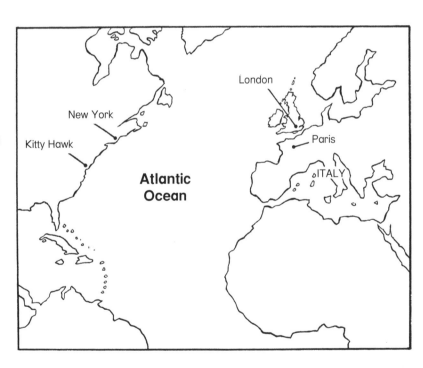

London

New York

Paris

Kitty Hawk

ITALY

Atlantic
Ocean

EXTENSION

Make a timeline for your school year. Put the important dates on
your timeline and say what each date is. (The start of the school
year? Sports day? The school fair? The holidays?) You can draw
little pictures on your timeline so it is easy to understand.

Understanding poems

Two poems

1 Something mysterious happens in each of the poems below.
Read this one.

Someone came knocking

Someone came knocking
    At my wee, small door;
Someone came knocking,
    I'm sure-sure-sure.
I listened, I opened,
    I looked to left and right,
But naught there was a-stirring
    In the still dark night.
 Only the busy beetle
    Tap-tapping in the wall,
Only from the forest
    The screech-owl's call.
Only the cricket whistling
    While the dewdrops fall,
So I know not who came knocking,
At all, at all, at all.

Walter de la Mare

2 Now read this poem and fill in the chart, using a tick or cross
in the first two columns.

What has happened to Lulu?

What has happened to Lulu, mother?
What has happened to Lu?
There's nothing in her bed but an old rag-doll
And by its side a shoe.

Why is her window wide, mother,
The curtain flapping free,
And only a circle on the dusty shelf
Where her money-box used to be?

Why do you turn your head, mother,
And why do tear drops fall?
And why do you crumple that note on the fire
And say it is nothing at all?

I woke to voices late last night,
I heard an engine roar.
Why do you tell me the things I heard
Were a dream and nothing more?

I heard somebody cry, mother,
In anger or in pain,
But now I ask you why, mother,
You say it was a gust of rain.

Why do you wander about as though
You don't know what to do?
What has happened to Lulu, mother?
What has happened to Lu?

Charles Causley

	Poem 1	Poem 2	Words or phrases that tell me this
The poem is about something that happened at night.			
The poet heard birds and insects.			
The poet heard voices.			
The poet asks someone about the strange noises.			
The weather was bad.			
In the end the poet solves the mystery.			

EXTENSION
Draw a picture of Lulu's bedroom from Poem 2. Include all the things you read about.

Interpreting diagrams

How pencils are made

Look at the drawings of how pencils are made. Next to each picture, write a sentence to explain it. Use words like: first, after that, then, finally.

First, they cut down the trees.

grooves

Pencil lead

The pencils are dipped ...

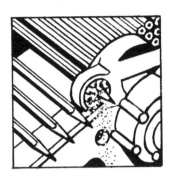

EXTENSION.
Can you imagine how fish fingers are made and brought to the table?
Make drawings, and next to each write a sentence to explain it.
Use these words: catch, sort, clean, cut into fingers, add breadcrumbs,
fry, freeze, pack, take to the shops, buy, cook, serve.

Icons

Reading the signs

Icons are signs that give us information without using words. They are easy to understand. Look at this icon.

a) Where might you see it? _____

b) What does the icon mean? _____

Where can you see these icons and what do they mean?

a) _____

b) _____

a) _____

b) _____

a) _____

b) _____

a) _____

b) _____

a) _____

b) _____

a) _____

b) _____

a) _____

b) _____

a) _____

b) _____

a) _____

b) _____

a) _____

b) _____

a) _____

b) _____

a) _____

b) _____

ExTeNSION

Think of three other icons you have seen. You may have seen them on clothing, on a computer or somewhere else. Draw one icon in each box. Ask a partner to write:

a) where you might find it   b) what the icon means.

a) _____

b) _____

a) _____

b) _____

a) _____

b) _____

Reading a calendar

Keeping up with the Jones family

1 Look at the Jones's calendar for the last six months of last year.
Use it to answer the True or False questions.

JULY	AUGUST	SEPTEMBER	OCTOBER	NOVEMBER	DECEMBER
1 Su	1 W	1 Sa	1 M	1 Th	1 Sa
2 M	2 Th	2 Su	2 Tu	2 F	2 Su
3 Tu	3 F	3 M	3 W	3 Sa	3 M
4 W	4 Sa	4 Tu	4 Th	4 Su	4 Tu
5 Th	5 Su	5 W *Back to school*	5 F	5 M	5 W
6 F	6 M	6 Th	6 Sa	6 Tu	6 Th
7 Sa	7 Tu	7 F	7 Su	7 W *Sarah to babysit 7 pm*	7 F
8 Su	8 W	8 Sa *Mitsuko to stay w/end*	8 M *Visit the farm*	8 Th	8 Sa
9 M	9 Th	9 Su	9 Tu	9 F	9 Su
10 Tu	10 F	10 M	10 W	10 Sa	10 M
11 W	11 Sa *Seaview, Devon for week*	11 Tu	11 Th	11 Su *Flight BA 2122 to Paris*	11 Tu
12 Th	12 Su	12 W	12 F	12 M	12 W
13 F	13 M	13 Th	13 Sa	13 Tu	13 Th
14 Sa	14 Tu	14 F	14 Su	14 W	14 F
15 Su	15 W	15 Sa	15 M *Half-term*	15 Th	15 Sa
16 M	16 Th	16 Su	16 Tu *Josh dental appointment*	16 F	16 Su
17 Tu	17 F	17 M	17 W	17 Sa	17 M
18 W	18 Sa	18 Tu	18 Th	18 Su	18 Tu
19 Th	19 Su	19 W	19 F	19 M	19 W
20 F *end of term*	20 M	20 Th *renew car insurance*	20 Sa	20 Tu	20 Th *School carol service*
21 Sa	21 Tu	21 F	21 Su	21 W	21 F
22 Su	22 W	22 Sa	22 M	22 Th	22 Sa
23 M	23 Th	23 Su	23 Tu	23 F	23 Su
24 Tu	24 F *Louis to vet*	24 M	24 W	24 Sa	24 M *Nanna arrives*
25 W	25 Sa	25 Tu	25 Th	25 Su	25 Tu
26 Th	26 Su	26 W	26 F	26 M	26 W
27 F	27 M	27 Th	27 Sa *Put clocks back one hour tonight!*	27 Tu	27 Th
28 Sa	28 Tu	28 F	28 Su	28 W	28 F
29 Su	29 W	29 Sa	29 M	29 Th	29 Sa
30 M	30 Th	30 Su	30 Tu	30 F	30 Su
31 Tu	31 F		31 W		31 M

True or False?

	True	False	If False, write the truth here
Term ended on 19 July.		✓	*Term ended ...*
The family spent Christmas alone.			
The cat was ill in the summer.			
The school carol service was on 19 December.			
A Japanese friend visited them in the third week in August.			
Mr and Mrs Jones went out on 7 November.			
The Joneses went away for half-term.			
The Joneses have a car.			
British Summer Time ends in October.			
The children had four weeks' holiday at the seaside.			
Someone in the family took the train to Paris in November.			
The family spent a week on holiday in August.			

2   Look at this tree in the four seasons. Write the correct season above each drawing.

EXTENSION
You've just returned from a week on planet Mars.
Write your diary for each day of the week,
Monday–Sunday. Start: On Monday I arrived by . . .

Comparing images

Spot the difference

The Burton family went to the cinema. When they left home, their living room looked like this.

1 Write a paragraph describing their living room. Write about the things in the box.

| cat   clock   armchair   vase |
| floor   window   picture |
| DVD player   DVDs |

When the Burtons got home from the cinema later that night, this is what they found.

2 Make a list of what is different about the living room.

The window ...

_____

_____

_____

_____

_____

_____

_____

_____

3 What do you think has happened? How do you know?

I think ...

_____

_____

_____

EXTENSION

You are one of the Burton children. Write a letter to a friend about what happened that night.

Interpreting diagrams

The Space Shuttle

1 Look at the pictures of the Space Shuttle trip into space and back.

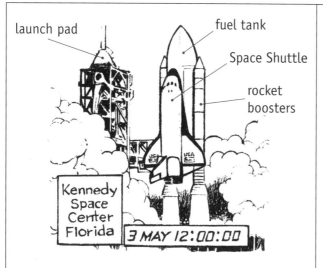

launch pad

fuel tank

Space Shuttle

rocket boosters

Kennedy Space Center Florida

3 MAY 12:00:00

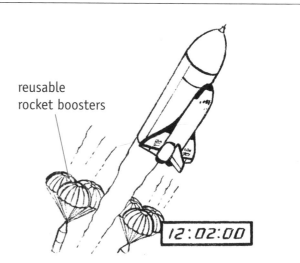

reusable rocket boosters

12:02:00

empty fuel tank

12:09:00

satellite for sending and receiving signals

solar panels for onboard electricity

living quarters

astronaut doing tests

engines to steer Shuttle

payload doors

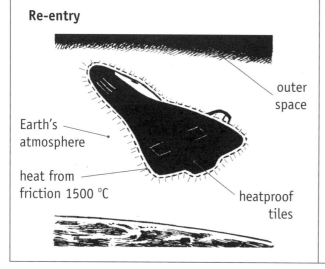

Re-entry

outer space

Earth's atmosphere

heat from friction 1500 °C

heatproof tiles

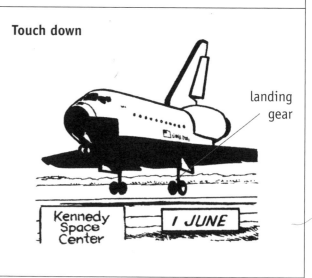

Touch down

landing gear

Kennedy Space Center

1 JUNE

2 Look at the story of the Space Shuttle's journey into space and answer these questions.

What country does the Space Shuttle lift off from? _____

_____

What time is lift off? _____

How long after lift off do its rocket boosters fall away? _____

Why do the rocket boosters have parachutes? _____

_____

Why does the Space Shuttle drop its fuel tank? _____

_____

When does it do so? _____

What instruments are inside the payload doors? _____

_____

What are these instruments for? _____

_____

Why does the Space Shuttle have heatproof tiles underneath? _____

_____

How long did the Space Shuttle spend in space? _____

_____

EXTENSION . . . .
Imagine you are an astronaut on the Space Shuttle.
Write about an exciting trip from lift off to touch
down. What was your job in space? Were you ever
scared? Were you glad to be back?

Bar charts and pie charts

Bullying in school

1 The pupils at Hopton School made a bar chart
to show bullying in years 1–4. Look at the chart
and answer the questions.

Which year group had the
most bullying?   _____

How many children in that
year group were bullied?   _____

Which year group had
the least bullying?   _____

How many children in that
year group were bullied?   _____

How many children were bullied
in total in the school?   _____

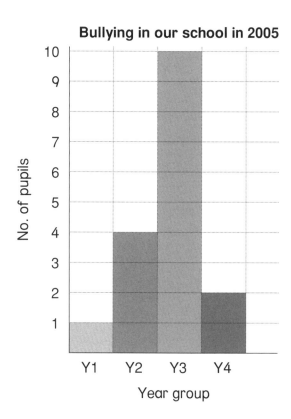

Bullying in our school in 2005

2 Now look at the chart the pupils made for 2007:

Which year group had the
most bullying?   _____

How many children in that
year group were bullied?   _____

Which year group had
the least bullying?   _____

How many children in that
year group were bullied?   _____

How many children were bullied
in total in the school?   _____

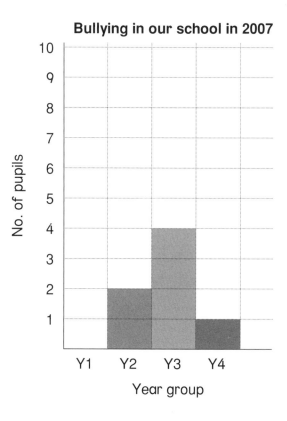

Bullying in our school in 2007

3   Use the two bar charts to complete the text.

In 2005 in Hopton School, a total of _____ children were bullied.

In 2007, only _____ children were bullied. Compared to 2005,
we can say that in 2007 there was <u>more/less</u> bullying in Hopton School.

4   There are 100 pupils in year 4.
Look at this pie chart about their pets
and answer these questions.

Which pets are most popular
with the year-4 pupils? _____

Which animal do fewest pupils
have? _____

Ten pupils have which pet? _____

What pets might you find
in the 'Other pets' section? _____

How many year-4 pupils have a pet at home? _____

How many have no pet at home? _____

Write the pets in order from most popular to least popular. _____

_____

Our pets

Cats: 25

Hamsters: 25

Dogs: 10

Other pets: 10

No pets: 20

Rabbits: 8

Guinea pigs: 2

5   Now complete this bar chart with
the information about the pets
in the pie chart.

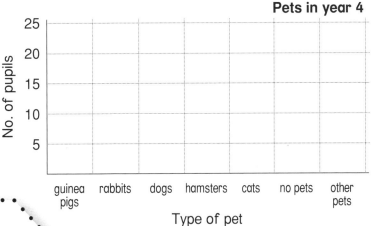

Pets in year 4

No. of pupils

25
20
15
10
5

guinea pigs rabbits dogs hamsters cats no pets other pets

Type of pet

ExTENSION
Collect information about
your classmates and make a
bar chart. It could be about their
favourite TV programme, the month
they were born in, the letter their
first/second name begins with.

Cross-section and mind map

Tsunami

Professor O'Brien is an expert on tsunamis. These are the images she prepared on her computer before giving a talk.

There are many tsunamis in Japan. They call it

津 = tsu   (harbour)

波 = nami (wave)

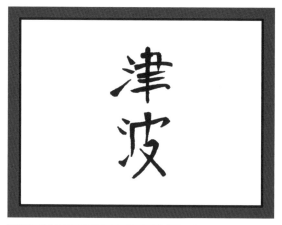

Tsunamis come with little warning.

This picture shows a beach in Sri Lanka on Boxing Day, 2004.

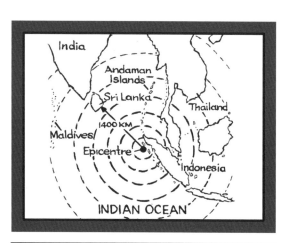

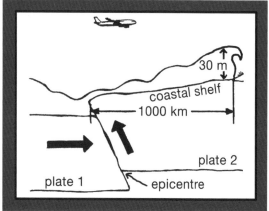

Use these words to complete Professor O'Brien's talk.

jet   plates   Indonesia   rock
Pacific Ocean   faster   opposite
deep   1000   epicentre   950 km
30 metres   sea   coastal shelf

1 Here is what Professor O'Brien said. Fill in the gaps in her talk.

Hello, everybody. Today I'm going to talk to you about tsunamis.

The word is Japanese. It means _____. How do tsunamis happen?

These pictures will help me explain. The Earth's surface is covered in massive areas of _____ called plates.
Well, sometimes the plates are forced to move in _____ directions by pressure in the rock.
The pressure may build up for millions of years. When the two _____ suddenly move, the result is an
earthquake. If this happens in the _____, the movement disturbs the water and causes a tsunami.
Waves immediately start to move outwards from the centre or _____ of the underwater earthquake.
As the waves travel, they get _____. They can reach speeds of _____ an hour – that's as fast
as a _____! On the surface, the water may seem calm, but deep down a massive wave is moving
towards the coast. That's why tsunamis seem to come without warning. The water rises up when the waves crash into
the shallow _____ – where the water is not so _____.
A tsunami wave can grow to a towering _____ – that's the height of a five-storey building! A powerful tsunami
happened on Boxing Day in 2004. Its epicentre was near _____ _____, and as
well as killing hundreds of thousands there, it killed an enormous number of people over _____ kilometres away
on the other side of the _____ in India and on the island of Sri Lanka.

2 Make a mind map with everything you know about tsunamis.

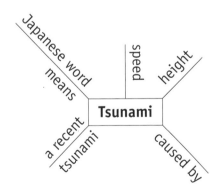

Japanese word
means
a recent
tsunami
speed
height
caused by
Tsunami

EXTENSION
What other natural disasters do you know about?
(Think of water, snow, wind, mud, mountains.) Make a list.
Which kind do you think causes the most damage? Say why.

Interpreting and completing a picture story

A day in the country

1 Look at the picture story and write what the characters said and thought in the bubbles. Don't forget to complete the storyline below the pictures.

One fine summer's day Gus, Chloe and Imran

Suddenly, Gus saw the most wonderful

In spite of the warning sign, _____

Next he _____

Soon _____

Chloe and Imran saw _____

Imran and Chloe managed _____

Only now was it clear _____

Gus couldn't believe it when _____

When night fell _____

2 What is the ending of the story? Draw what happened here.
Use speech and thought bubbles.

EXTENSION
Draw your own story with speech and thought
bubbles. Here are some words to use under each box.
One day / Suddenly / Just then / Later / Little did he
know that / She couldn't believe it when …

Reading a family tree

The generation game

1 Look at the family tree for five generations of a family and answer the questions.

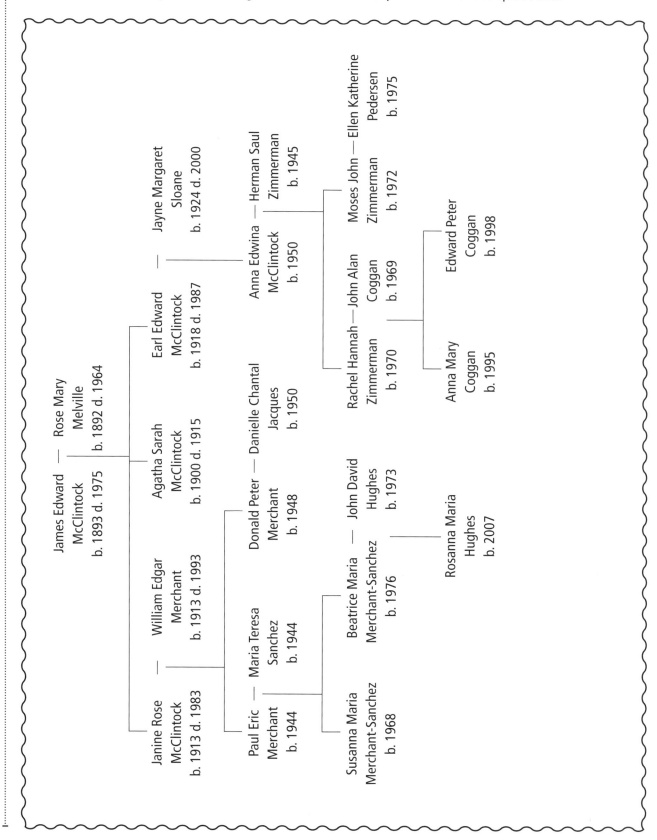

When was James McClintock born? _____1893_____

At what age did James McClintock die? _____

What was James McClintock's wife's surname before she married him? _____

Whom did Janine McClintock marry? _____

What is the name of Janine McClintock's only brother? _____

What is the relationship between Agatha and Janine McClintock? _____

How many children did Agatha McClintock have? _____

What is the name of James McClintock's oldest grandson? _____

How many children does this grandson have? _____

Are they male or female? _____

What is the first name of Susanna Merchant-Sanchez's sister? _____

What relation is Susanna Merchant-Sanchez to little Rosanna Hughes? _____

How did the name Zimmerman get into the McClintock family tree? _____

_____

How many children does Herman Zimmerman have? _____

2 Make the connection.

Find Anna Coggan on the family tree. How old is she now? _____
Draw a line on the family tree connecting Anna Coggan to:

a) her younger brother

b) her baby cousin

c) her Uncle Moses and Aunty Ellen

d) her great-great-grandmother.

EXTENSION · · · · · · · · · · · · · · ·
You could make a family tree for
your own family. How many generations
back can you go? Instead, you could
draw pictures of five people from the
family tree. What do you think they
might look like? Label each picture
with names and dates.

Icons

At an airport

1 At an international airport where people speak different languages, we need icons everyone can understand. Write the correct word from the list with its icon.

Currency exchange   Lift
Baggage reclaim   Lost and found
Telephone   Baby changing
Luggage trolleys   Meeting point
Departures   Passport control
Arrivals   Toilets

1 *Departures*

2

3

4

5

6

7

8

9

10

11

12

Safari park

2 You are an icon painter in a wild animal park.
Invent icons to warn visitors of these dangers:

a) Danger of slipping on monkeys' banana peels.

b) Block your nose! Smelly skunks about.

c) Stay in vehicles! Dangerous tigers on the loose.

d) Caution! Elephants may squirt water from their trunks.

a	b
c	**d**

EXTENSION
Invent icons for other dangers in the safari park!

Seasons and change

Looking for clues

1 What season does this picture show? _____

Draw four things in this picture which tell you this.

a)	b)
c)	d)

2 Draw the same scene in one other season. Show what has changed.

3 Draw what happens later in these scenes.

a)

b)

4 Draw what happened before these scenes.

a)

b)

EXTENSION
Compose two pictures for a partner and ask them to draw what happened before/after what you have shown.

Then and now

Say 'Cheese'

This Victorian family has had their picture taken.

Write down as many differences as you can see between how people lived then and how we live today.

a) *Man wears top hat.*

b)

c)

d)

e)

f)

g)

h)

i)

j)

Imagine a family has had their picture taken today, showing how they travel.

How would each family member dress and look?

How would we take the picture?

Draw the scene here.

EXTENSION

Imagine a family of the future, two hundred years from today. What will they dress and look like? How will they travel? Draw them!

Old fashioned and modern

How they used to live

1 Look at these old-fashioned things from the past. We still use these things today, but they look very different. Next to each old-fashioned object, draw what it looks like today.

Old fashioned	Modern

Old fashioned	Modern

Aerial view to plan

A plan of Hopetown

Look at this drawing of Hopetown from above.

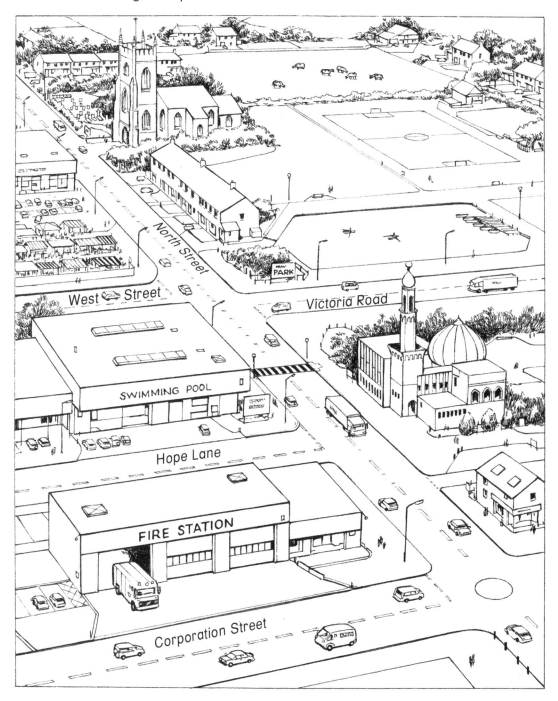

1 Find these places in the town.
Label the picture:

fire station	Market Square
Victoria Park	St Andrew's Church
swimming pool	Mosque
boating lake	Common

2 Now complete this plan of the town, adding the road names and labelling the buildings and open spaces from the picture on page 47.

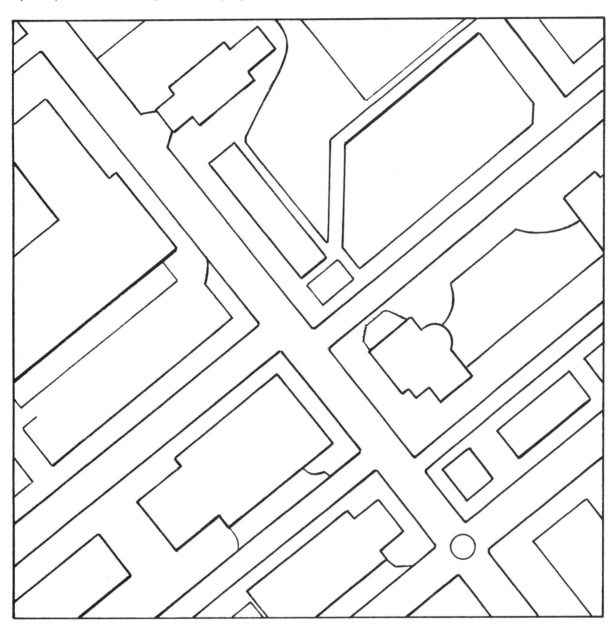

EXTENSION
Draw a plan of your neighbourhood. Write in the street or road names, and show your house and any other important places.

Cutaway diagram to plan

1   Look at these drawings of No. 3, Cherry Avenue.
The roof is off so you can see the upstairs and downstairs rooms clearly.

Downstairs

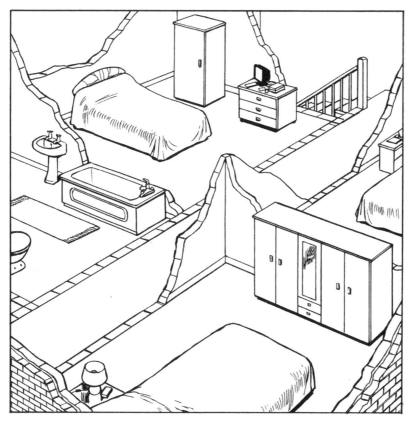

Upstairs

2 Answer these questions about the house.

a) How many bedrooms does it have? _____

b) What is above the kitchen? _____

c) Which room has been added? _____

d) Which room is next to the kitchen? _____

3 This is the plan for No. 3, Cherry Avenue.
Decide which is the upstairs and which the downstairs plan.
Write in the name of each room on the plans.

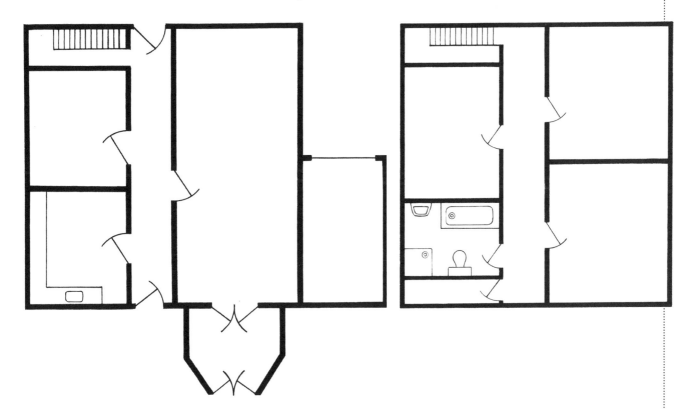

EXTENSION

Draw a plan of the upstairs or downstairs of your home and label the rooms. If you live on one level, draw all of your home.

Interpreting a table

Kitchen contents

1 The person who counted the items on this list of kitchen contents has made some mistakes. Look at the drawing and put a tick if the number is correct. Correct what is wrong.

Item	Number	Correction
Teacups	4	3
Mugs	2	
Dinner plates	5	
Cereal bowls	2	
Milk jug	1	
Teapot	1	
Colander	1	
Drinking glasses	3	
Wine glasses	4	
Electric carving knife	1	
Apron	1	
Saucepans	3	
Salad bowl	3	
Frying pan	1	
Infant's high chair	1	
Electric toaster	1	
Fridge	1	
Microwave	0	
Electric cooker	1	
Broom	1	
Dustpan and brush	1	
Mop	1	
Bucket	1	
Electric blender	0	
Catflap	1	
Dog basket	1	
Cooker hood	1	
Window blinds	2	
Picture	1	

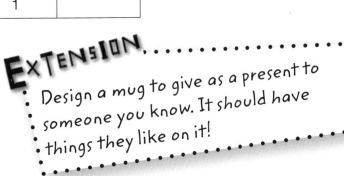

EXTENSION

Design a mug to give as a present to someone you know. It should have things they like on it!

Narrative

What happened?

1 Complete the drawings to show what happened.

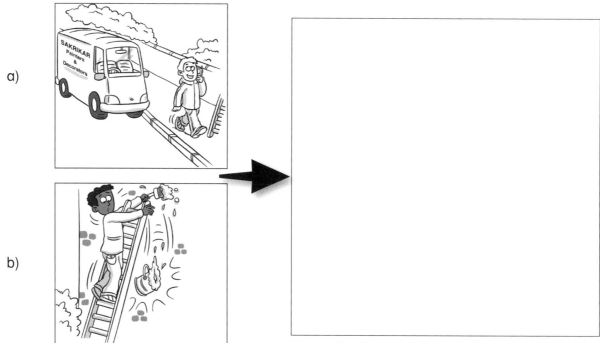

Draw what happened next here.

Draw what happened next here.

Draw what happened next here.

Draw what happened next here.

EXTENSION ....
Draw three or four pictures to tell a funny story of your own.

Bar chart

On the beach

1 When class 4 went on a trip to the seaside, the pupils all did different things.

The bar chart shows the number of boys
and the number of girls who did different things.

Key: = boys

= girls

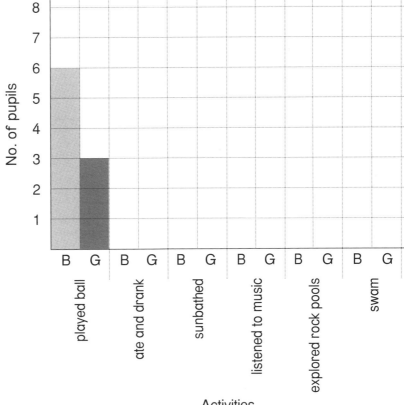

No. of pupils

8
7
6
5
4
3
2
1

B G   B G   B G   B G   B G   B G

played ball   ate and drank   sunbathed   listened to music   explored rock pools   swam

Activities

How many boys played ball? _____

How many girls played ball? _____

2 Now fill in the bar chart for all the other activities for boys and for girls.

EXTENSION

Design a table to show the number of boys and the number of girls who did each activity. Add fun icons for each activity on your chart so it's easy to understand!

Class 4	Boys	Girls
Swam	5	5

Permission to Photocopy

Upside-down and mirror images

What will you see?

1 a) Look at this triangle.

Draw it upside down here.

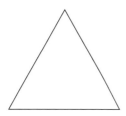

b) This is Patch the dog. What's different about how she looks in the mirror?

Patch

Patch in the mirror

_____

_____

_____

_____

_____

c) These skyscrapers stand beside a river. Draw their reflection in the water here.

2 Look at these pictures.

 Upright

 Upright mirror image

 Upside down

 Upside-down mirror image

3 Draw this trainer in the same four positions as the example.

Normal view

Mirror image

Upside down

Upside-down mirror image

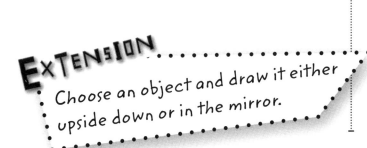

EXTENSION

Choose an object and draw it either upside down or in the mirror.

Abstract concepts

Draw the opposite

1 In the space under each drawing write the word that describes it. Then draw something showing the word's opposite in the column on the right. Write the word for the opposite underneath your drawing.

1 *dirty*

2

3

4

5

EXTENSION
Think of a feeling you have had. Draw that feeling so everyone will understand it. Then draw the opposite of that feeling.